BIG MAD® ON CAMPUS

Edited by
Albert B. Feldstein

A Warner Communications Company

WARNER BOOKS EDITION

For information address:
E. C. Publications, Inc.,
485 Madison Avenue,
New York, N.Y. 10022

This Warner Books Edition is published by arrangement with E. C. Publications, Inc.

Designed by Thomas Nozkowski.

Warner Books, Inc.,
666 Fifth Avenue,
New York, N.Y. 10103

A Warner Communications Company

Printed in the United States of America

First Warner Books Printing:
October, 1983

10 9 8 7 6 5 4 3 2 1

KEEP ON TREKIN'

TV being the ridiculous industry it is, no one should be surprised that the hottest show around is one that folded eight years ago. We mean, of course, "Star Trek," which is being kept alive by tens of thousands of dedicated, fanatic "Trekkies." Considering "Star Trek's" popularity, it's only a matter of time before someone turns it into a Broadway Musical. So, before that happens, we'll do it first, with

THE MAD "STAR TREK" MUSICAL

ARTIST: MORT DRUCKER WRITER: FRANK JACOBS

Captain's Log—Stardate: 10-5-76! Through an incredible time warp, the crew of the Starship "Improvise" has been summoned by some mysterious power to a meeting back aboard the retired ship eight years after the death of the show!
*Isn't it strange? After eight years— Him playing Captain again— Me with my ears! Send in the crew!
Look at me now— At my old post— Happy that I can forget "Barbary Coast!" Where is my crew? Send in my crew!
See our old ship— Down from the sky! None of the engines Are working, And neither am I!
Once I was saving Their lives with My medical skill! Where am I now? Over the hill!
How have we done? Not well, we fear— Typecast as spacemen, Which means... We've no career! So send in the crew! This old, washed-up crew! We're better off here!

*Sung to the tune of "*Send In The Clowns*"

Schlock, doesn't being back here fill you with **nostalgia?**
You **forget,**Captain Quirk, that **Vulcans** are **unemotional,** and that if I **were** nostalgic, I would be **showing emotion!** However, being here **DOES** fill me with a sense of **awe!**
That once we all roamed through the **frontiers of space** in this ship?
No . . . that I've **bombed out** in **every role** since I took off these **ears!**
As long as we're all **here,** let's re-create what life was **really like** in space! The **boredom** between **adventures!**
The **disgust** at seeing the **same faces** year after year!
The fact that **most** planets are **incredibly dull!**
As you wish!

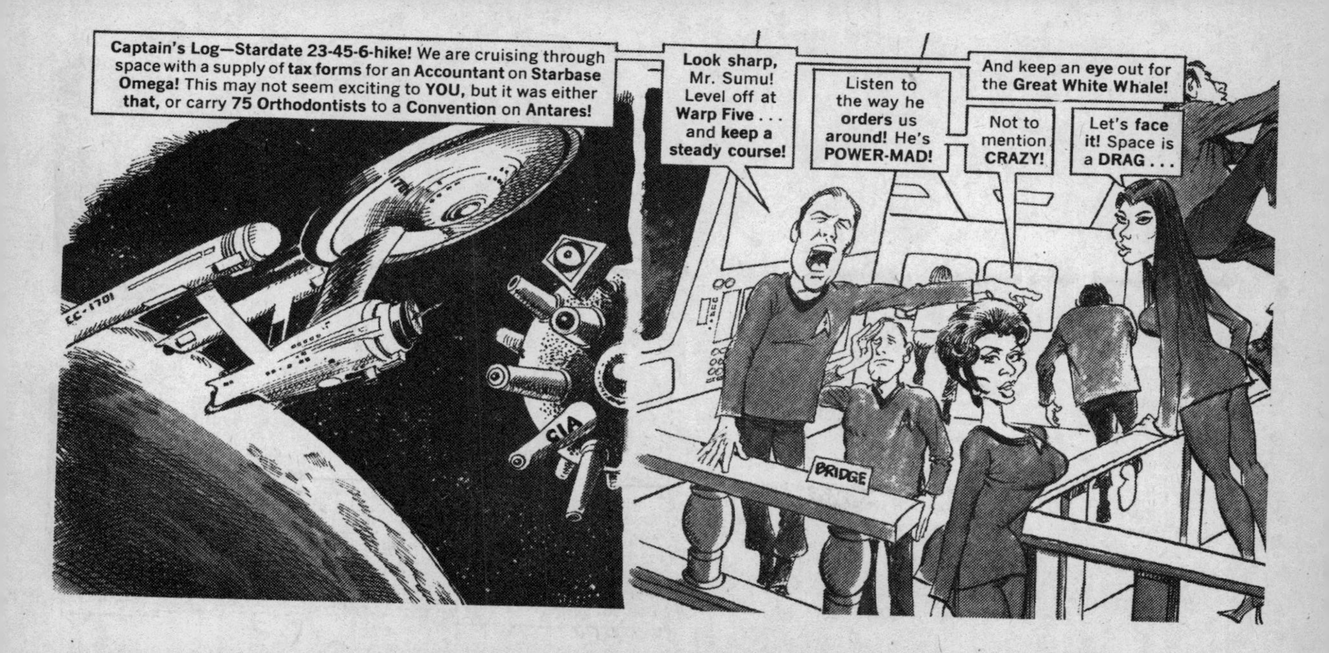
Captain's Log—Stardate 23-45-6-hike! We are cruising through space with a supply of tax forms for an Accountant on Starbase Omega! This may not seem exciting to YOU, but it was either that, or carry 75 Orthodontists to a Convention on Antares!
Look sharp, Mr. Sumu! Level off at Warp Five . . . and keep a steady course!
And keep an eye out for the Great White Whale!
Listen to the way he orders us around! He's POWER-MAD!
Not to mention CRAZY!
Let's face it! Space is a DRAG . . .
CC-1701
CIA
BRIDGE

*What do you get when you fly through space?
You're locked in a ship and don't feel human,
Cooped up in space with smelly crewmen—
I-I'll...never fly through space again-n-n—
I'll never fly through space again!
What do you eat when you fly through space?
Those heat-n-serve meals from Starbase Alpha,
Tasting like hunks of dried alfalfa—
I-I'll...never fly through space again-n-n—
I'll never fly through space again!

I'd rather join the un-em-ployed
Than cir-cle some stu-pid ast-er-oid!
Watchin' some stupid planet dyin'
Somewhere out there in East Orion!

*Sung to the tune of "*I'll Never Fall In Love Again*"

What do you do when you fly through space?
You twiddle your thumbs and you count the hours;
Then when you're through, you take cold showers—
I-I'll...never fly through space again-n-n—
I'll never fly through space again!

*Sung to the tune of "*The Age Of Aquarius*"

Minor actors that you bring on
Perish when they meet a Klingon!
One-time players not seen later
Vanish in a planet's crater!
Those of us who try to aid them
Fail because the script has made them
Dis-pens-i-ble!
DIS-PENS-I-BLE!
CAPTAIN!! The ship can't TAKE any more!
You mean . . . the SUPERSTRUCTURE can't stand our incredible speed?!
No . . . the CREW can't stand your terrible singing! We're close to a MUTINY!!
Dr. McGoy, I think I've got a ruptured appendix!
Take it out yourself! I'm just not interested in trite, hackneyed Earth ailments any more!

*I'm a doctor out in space,
And, like, I really groove this place,
Because of all the rare dis-ease-es—
Not like your silly coughs or sneezes!
Treating ail-ments that no man be-fore has seen
Is real keen—
They are my kinds...of sick-ness!
Observe that crewman rub his leg;
Last week he got the Neptune Plague;
Today his joints are blue and yel-low—
In seven days he'll turn to Jel-lo—
And that last re-main-ing blob I'll an-a-lyze
When he dies—
This is my kind...of sick-ness!

While beaming up from Gamma II,
I thought this man had caught the flu;
But then his mouth was growing fangs there—
And now from ceilings he just hangs there—
As I sit and list-en to his last re-quests,
I'll run tests—
This is my kind . . . of sick-ness!
Oh, what a joy it is to see
Each brand-new unknown mal-a-dy—
These men are pleading, "Won't you cure us
"From what we picked up on Arc-tur-us?"
And with ev-ry dy-ing gurg-gle in their throats,
I'll make notes—
These are my kinds...of sick-ness!
*Sung to the tune of "The Sound Of Silence"

There's only ONE THING I love better than a space disease, and that's baiting Mr. Schlock!
Hey, Schlock! Why does a Vulcan have pointed ears?
I . . . I don't know! Why . . . ?
So he can count to twelve!
ANOTHER "Vulcan Joke"! How long must I put up with this mockery?! If only these clods knew how a Vulcan really feels!
*It's having pointed ears and hearing crewmen telling Vulcan jokes on ship;
And it's always playing straight-man to McGoy, who thinks I'm something of a freak;
And it's chatting with computers and discovering I bore them and they're only chatting back just to be kind;
And it's reaching the conclusion that I'm looked on as a weirdo and a Vulcan's life is nothing but a grind!

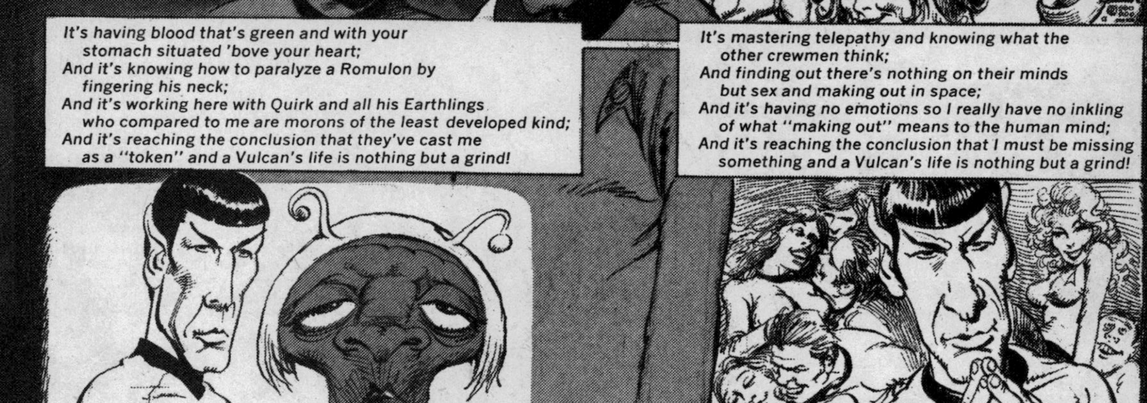
It's having blood that's green and with your stomach situated 'bove your heart; And it's knowing how to paralyze a Romulon by fingering his neck; And it's working here with Quirk and all his Earthlings who compared to me are morons of the least developed kind; And it's reaching the conclusion that they've cast me as a "token" and a Vulcan's life is nothing but a grind!
It's mastering telepathy and knowing what the other crewmen think; And finding out there's nothing on their minds but sex and making out in space; And it's having no emotions so I really have no inkling of what "making out" means to the human mind; And it's reaching the conclusion that I must be missing something and a Vulcan's life is nothing but a grind!
*Sung to the tune of "Gentle On My Mind"

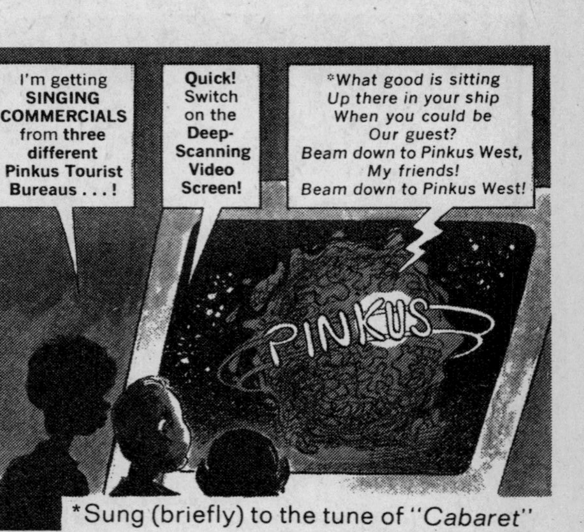

*Sung (briefly) to the tune of "*Cabaret*"

*Sung (briefly) to the tune of "Yesterday"

*How many spots out in space have hotels
That are on the Am-er-i-can Plan?
Yes, how many spots have a bi-nar-y sun
Where a guy gets a two-sided tan?
Yes, how many spots can you name with great broads
That go wild for a pointed-ear man?
The answer, my friends, is here on Pinkus South!
The answer is here in Pinkus South!
Well, Mr. Schlock . . . ?
I don't know about YOU, Captain, but I'm beaming down to Pinkus South!
*Sung (briefly) to the tune of "Blowing In The Wind"
There could be trouble, so put your phasers on "Stun"!
According to my Tricorder Reading, the inhabitants are BEAUTIFUL YOUNG WOMEN!
In that case . . . put your phasers on "Caress"!
WAS HERE

I am Varma, Queen of Pinkus, Darling of the Galaxy, Goddess of the Song-Cue! I have the power to grant you and your crew immortality!
Us? Immortal? With our ratings, we won't even last the Season!!
You will never die, because—
*When you're has-sled
By your network,
And your ratings
Turn to rubble,
Don't despair if
You can't get work;
There's an ans-wer
To your troub-le—
Re-runs!
You'll stay immortal with
Re-runs!
You'll live forever on
Re-runs!
Lasting for
Years on
TV!
When fresh plots are
Hard to dream up
And each dis-tant
Star you've been to,
Don't fret when they
Split your team up;
You'll survive by
Get-ting in-to
*Sung to the tune of "Call Me"

Re-runs!
You'll stay immortal with
Re-runs!
You'll live forever on
Re-runs!
Lasting for years on TV!
Life will be juic-y!
You'll out-do Luc-y!
When your old shows are re-played!
No one can stop . . . you!
They won't dare drop . . . you!
And, like, man, you'll have it made!
When you see your
Youth-ful face go,
And you're fat and
Dis-si-pat-ed,
You can still through
Deep-est space go,
Young and slim and
Syn-di-cat-ed!
Re-runs!
You'll stay immortal with
Re-runs!
You'll live forever on
Re-runs!
Lasting for
years on
TV!

Captain's Log—Stardate: 54-40 or fight! Our **flashback** is **over** and we're back where we were when this musical **started**—still waiting for that **mysterious power** who summoned us together **eight years** after the **death** of our show!

Sorry to keep you **waiting,** Gentlemen! Now, let's get right down to business . . .

So **YOU'RE** the **Mysterious Power!!**

That's **right!** I'm a **Vice-President** of **NBC!** We want you and your crew to **fly through space again . . . coast to coast** . . . on **Network Prime Time!**

Are you **crazy?** We'd be **out of our minds!** We're **sitting pretty** the way we **are!**

We're **idolized** by **thousands of Sci-Fi fans!** We're **mobbed** by **gorgeous teen-age "Trekkies"!**

We've got it **made** with **RE-RUNS** and **LECTURES** and **CONVENTIONS!** With **ROYALTIES** pouring in from **BOOKS** and **MODELS** and **TOYS** and **POSTERS!**

We don't need **YOU!** We've got—

*Money! That's the reason We don't have a care! Money! Oh, yessiree, we Really get our share!
See the Trekkies out there Who are buying our stuff; They're hooked, we swear, And that's enough!
Yes, Money Coming Through— We love You!
Money! Piling up in Big, e-nor-mous stacks! Money! From the sales of Kits and pap-er-backs!
Let's cheer those kids Who go in hock From buy-ing dolls Of Mr. Schlock!
Oh, Money! We love You! Yes, we Do!
*Sung to the tune of "Sunny"

A MAD Look At The TENNIS SET

ARTIST & WRITER:
PAUL PETER PORGES

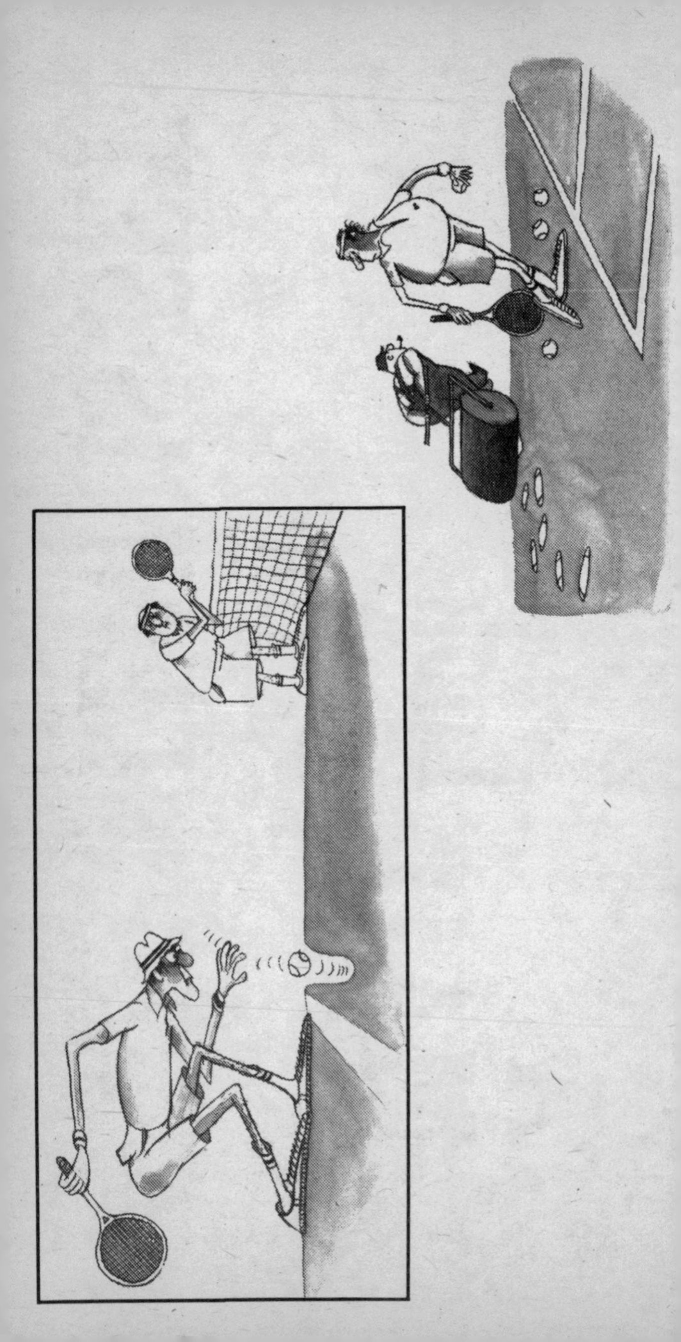

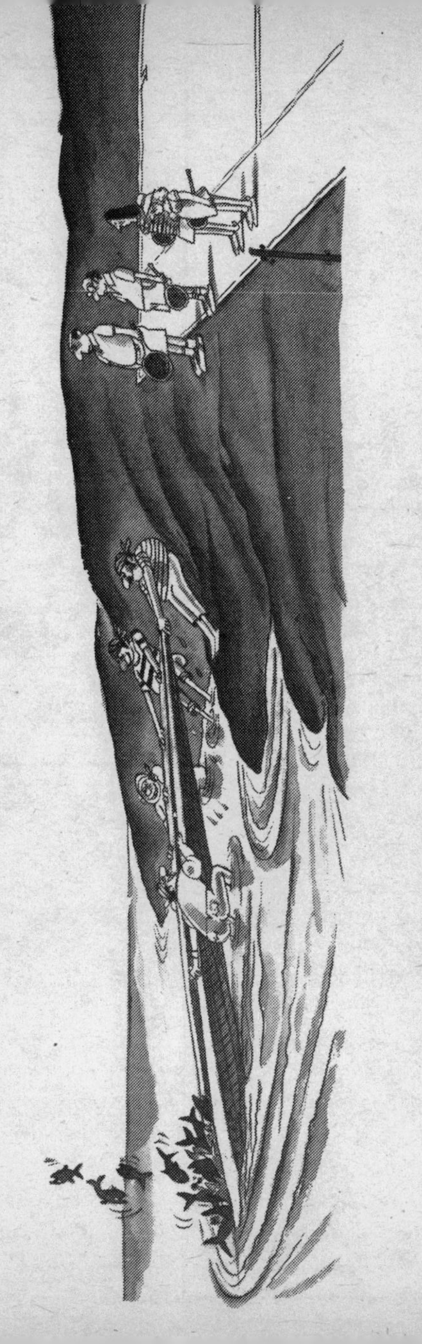

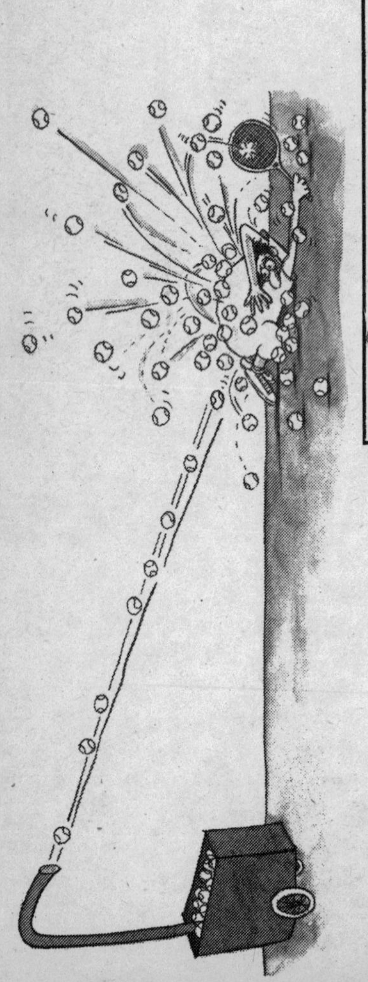

1
2

BUS
STOP

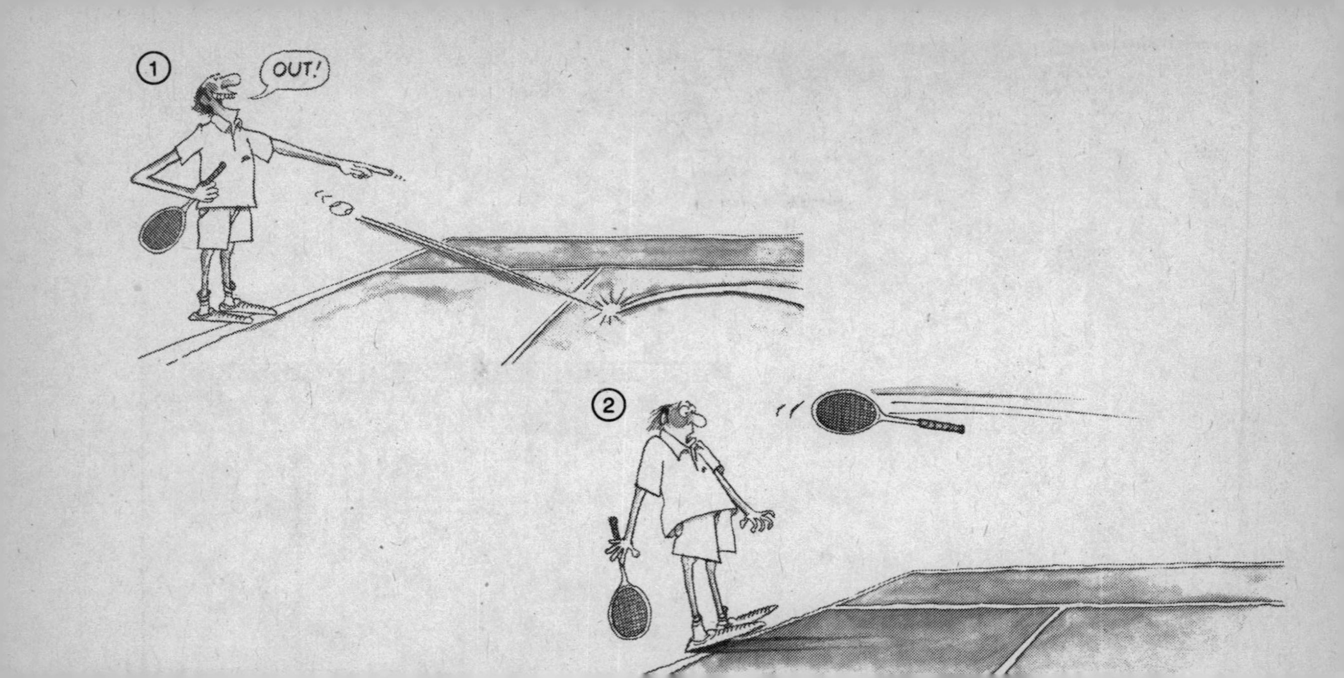
1
OUT!
2

1
2

BERG'S-EYE VIEW DEPT.

THE LIGHTER SIDE OF...

LIVING

TOGETHER

ARTIST & WRITER: DAVE BERG

Thanks a heap! You got the athroom **all steamed up!** Now I'll have to wait **ANOTHER** half hour before it **clears!!**

Great! A half hour is **all I'll need!!**

THERE'S A CROOK IN THIS DORM!!
My Mother sent me a box of cookies this morning, and some crud stole the whole batch!! Well, the guy that ate them better 'fess up!!

Yecch! Look at your clothes!! They're filthy!
So I'm a Grease Monkey! What do you expect?!?
I expect you to SHARE in the Household Chores!
Okay, what do you want me to do!?
You can start by doing your share of the Wash!!
I already DID!!
I got it DIRTY!!

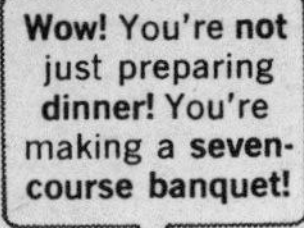
Wow! You're not just preparing dinner! You're making a seven-course banquet!

Not exactly! It's just that each member of the family likes different things!

My Husband is a "Steak a
Potatoes" man! Nancy is
"Vegetarian"! Leonard is
"Health Food" nut and Ala
insists upon eating "Fish"

And what kind of food do YOU eat??
With THIS family... WHAT ELSE?!

LEFTOVERS!!

WHAT. . . may I ask . . . are you doing?!?
I'm washing out the milk bottles!

And NOW WHAT. . . may I ask . . . are you doing?
Putting the caps back on! Then I'll put the bottles outside for the milkman to pick up!

nd he's going to bring them ack to a bottling plant where ey're going to throw away the aps and thoroughly sterilize the bottles!! Do you realize what you're doing is STUPID?

I'd rather YOU think I'm STUPID than the people at the BOTTLING PLANT think I'm a SLOB!!

The telephone and electric bills are overdue, and the checking account is overdrawn! Can't you keep a budget?!?
Don't yell at me! With your salary and the constant rise in prices, it's IMPOSSIBLE!!

Look, let's not fight! We're in a financial pickle! We nee money fast! Your Father live with us, and he's got mone Why don't you borrow some?
Well, okay. . . I'll t

Pop, I'm really strapped for cash! And I haven't the slightest idea where I'm going to get it from!
Good! I'm glad to hear that!

For a minute there, I thought you had some idea you were going to borrow it from ME!

I don't mean to offend, but your Wife isn't a very good HOUSEKEEPER!
Really?!? I guess I never noticed! I spend most of my time in my basement workshop!

Actually, I've always thought of her as a NEATNESS NUT!!

Magazine articles advise women to "put the ROMANCE back in your marriage! When your Husband comes home, don't greet him in curlers and a dirty apron! Look your best for a change!" Well . . . that's exactly what I'm going to do!

Okay!! What's going on?!
OH!! You—you surprised me! You're home early today!!

That's right! And how come I find you all spiffed up?!?
I thought I'd try putting the romance back in our marriage!

Is that all?! Thank God! For a minute, I thought we were going out to dinner!!

But it's our **children** who are **divorced** and have **moved back in** with **their children** who are **doing** the **rattling around!**

Gladys, I am sick and tired of eating HAMBURGERS! Just for a change, how about lamb chops for supper tonight!?!
Gladys, that dripping kitchen faucet is driving me out of my mind! I wish SOMEBODY would put a new washer in it!
Huh?? Hey, what's with them?
They haven't spoken to each other in months! Communication would've broken down altogether if it weren't for Gladys!
Who's Gladys?
Their TURTLE!

For the life of me, I can't make up my mind, so you've got to help me! Which one of these swatches for the living room drapes do you like . . . the plaid, the art nouveau or the solid color?

Hmmmm! To tell you the truth, I can't decide!
You can't decide?!? The big businessman who's supposed to be able to make fast, firm decisions?! You CAN'T DECIDE!?

Okay! Okay! You want me to make a fast, firm decision?! Here it is!!

YOU DECIDE!!

GIN!
Again? Nobody can be that lucky!!
Hold it!! Are you accusing me of cheating?!
You bet I am! I don't know how you're doing it, but you are! And I never want to play cards with you again!
. . . Oh, yeah?!? Well, I never want to play cards with a SORE LOSER again! I'm going back to my room . . .

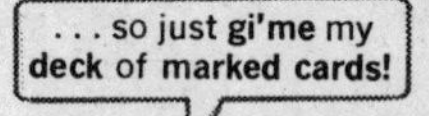
. . . so just gi'me my deck of marked cards!

Living with you is maddening!! I work like a dog making you a delicious meal . . . and you come home when you please! Now, it's gonna be overcooked because I have to warm it all up again!

And another thing! We have a HAMPER! So why don't you USE it instead of throwing things all over the floor!
There you go, making noises like a WIFE again!

But I AM a Wife!
I know!! And if you don't like me the way I am . . .
. . . go back to your HUSBAND!!
David Berg

ONE AFTERNOO
RUNNIN

WHILE

AN ERRAND

MILK

GROCERY
D.MARTIN...

THE ERA OF OUR WAYS DEPT.

In the beginning, Adam and Eve had two sons Cain and Abel . . . and thus formed the world' first family. And from them, Mankind receive a wonderful Legacy and a Code of Living tha has served families for generations, namely (a) Don't talk to snakes! . . . and (b) If you brother bugs you, hit him with a rock! But i some things remain the same, others change– particularly in the U.S. in the 20th century So join us now as MAD Magazine examines . .

. . . FROM THE EARLY 1900'S

. . . THROUGH THE MIDDLE 1900'S

. . . RIGHT O UP TO TODA

THE CHANGING ATTITUDES OF THE AMERICAN FAMILY

ARTIST: GEORGE WOODBRIDGE   WRITER: LARRY SIEGEL

SEX

EARLY 1900'S During this period, hardly anyone in the family ever discussed the subject of Sex.

But I'm nineteen years old! Isn't it about time you told me about sex?!
SEX?!? Why, you dirty, rotten, evil, disgusting foul-mouthed young lady!
Henry! That is no way to talk to your WIFE!!

MIDDLE 1900'S Then, people talked about Sex. There was only one problem: They had it all wrong!

But all along, I thought the STORK brings the baby, and that's it!
God, are you stupid! Didn't you ever hear of SEX?!? First of all, the man . . . bzzzz bzzzz . . . And then the woman . . . bzzz bzzz . . . And then the two of them . . . bzzz bzzzz bzzzz bzzz bzzzz . . .
Really?! No kidding? And then what?!?
And THEN the Stork brings the baby!!

...AND TODAY

Nowadays, of course, everybody talks about Sex, everybody knows about it, and practically everybody's doing it.

RELIGION

EARLY 1900'S During this period, just about everybody went to Church...

MIDDLE 1900'S Then, people weren't going to Church quite as often as before. And even when they DID go, some weird things were happening...

...AND TODAY

If you can believe it...nowadays, even WEIRDER things are happening!

RESPECT

EARLY 1900'S

In this period, the Family was ruled by a dictatorial, powerfully built, strong masculine presence—the American Father.

TODAY, WE WILL VISIT MY MOTHER IN NEW JERSEY! IS THAT CLEAR?!
Yes, Harold!
Yes, Father!
Yes, Sir!

MIDDLE 1900'S

With a growing permissiveness and independence within the Family structure, the Father, in an effort to be fair, no longer commanded. Now, he asked. The only trouble was...nobody answered!

Hey, gang! What say we visit Granny in New Jersey? Okay, scratch that! What say she visits us from New Jersey? Okay, then it's settled! We'll meet her half-way, like in the middle of the Lincoln Tunnel, and wave!
Now, what say I buy her a car first . . . so she doesn't get killed?!?

Nowadays, in a sense, we have returned to some old fashioned values. Once again, the Family is ruled by a dictatorial, powerfully built, strong masculine presence, mainly the American Mother!

TODAY, WE WILL VISIT MY MOTHER IN PHILADELPHIA! IS THAT CLEAR?
Yes, Agatha!
Yes, Mother!
Yes, Sir!

MENTAL PROBLEMS

EARLY 1900'S During this period, there was a very simple way to treat mental problems.

I don't know what's wrong with me! I'm so depressed lately! I—I think I'm on the verge of a nervous breakdown!
All you need is a change of scene! How'd you like to go to CONEY ISLAND
But you know how I hate the beach! That awful sand! That dirty ocean! That burning sun!
Okay, then how'd you like to go to a Lunatic Asylum?
BY THE SEA, BY THE SEA, BY THE BEAUTIFUL SEA . . .

MIDDLE 1900'S Folks were more realistic about Mental Health. Psychoanalysis was popular, and people were a lot richer for it. Mainly, the Psychiatrists.

Doctor . . . I've been seeing you three times a week at $25.00 a visit for the last ten years! When am I ever going to be CURED?!?
Your hour is up! We'll discuss it next time!
Next time! It's always next time! Well, there's not going to BE a next time! I've had it! It's like throwing money down a toilet!
NOW you're CURED!
I am? Then how come I feel lousy!
We'll discuss it next time!

...AND TODAY

Nowadays, Psychiatry is gradually being phased out. Because people are better adjusted now?!? You gotta be kidding!!

PROFANITY

EARLY 1900'S In those days, very few kids used Profanity. And if they ever did, the roof would fall in.

What's going on, Abigail?
Little Theodore said a **dirty word** and Mother is washing out his **mouth** with **soap** and **water.**

MIDDLE 1900'S Then, ALL kids were using Profanity, except they'd never dare use it around the house...

What are you **doing** in there, Marvin . . .?!
Smoking a **cigarette** . . . drinking **booze** . . . reading a **dirty book** . . . and **other** things!
All right . . . that's nice . . . as long as you **don't curse!**

...AND TODAY Nowadays, it isn't even worth discussing...

LEISURE TIME

EARLY 1900'S

In this period, families used to gather together in the living room and have all kinds of fun among themselves...

All right, everybody! First, we make some **taffy!** Then we look at some pictures of **Atlantic City** through the **stereopticon.** And then we gather around the **piano** and sing stirring **sea chanteys!**
I think it's a **grand** idea!
I think this will be our **best** New Year's Eve **ever!**
I think I'm gonna **throw up!**

MIDDLE 1900'S

With the advent of television, families gathered in the living room, but they were so engrossed in the tiny 7-inch screen that they hardly paid any attention to each other...or anything else.

Well, kids, we've been watching **17 straight hours of TV!** Next is **"Howdy Doody,"** then comes **"Kukla, Fran and Ollie,"** then we'll watch **Uncle Milty** and . . . Oh, golly, **we've** been dominating the set **long enough . . .**
MARY! WHAT WOULD **YOU** LIKE TO SEE?
I'd like to see that **television set** thrown into the **GARBAGE!!**
What **channel** is **THAT** on?

...AND TODAY

Once again, as in the good old days, families are gathering in living rooms and having fun among themselves. There's only one problem: Sometimes, the families are a little mixed up.

CAREERS

In those days, most boys' Careers were planned long in advance...usually by their Fathers...

Isn't little Benjamin cute . . . smashing his toys!
He sure is! And some day, he'll do a bully job—working for me at the Post Office!
You think he'll be able to do that with Parcel Post packages?
The REAL test will come when they're marked "Fragile"!

MIDDLE 1900'S

With the GI Bill of Rights after World War II, and a booming economy, many boys were able to go to college and to choose their own Careers.

Well, Son! What big plans have you got in mind, now that I've invested my life's savings . . . putting you through college?
First of all, I'm going to check the pages and pages of Want Ads in the N.Y. Times for all the employers eagerly looking for college graduates who majored in "Basket Weaving" and "Medieval Plumbing" . . .

...AND TODAY

With the Rock Music Industry where it is today, many young people have no problem at all with their Careers. But hiring good help is tough.

DRESS

EARLY 1900'S

In those days, most people dressed very fancy and wore tons of clothes. For instance, women wore corsets and girdles and eight petticoats and three hoop skirts and God knows what else.

Isn't it awful?! Her husband had a heart attack and died on the first night of their Honeymoon . . .!
The stress and strain of sex was too much for him . . .?
What sex?!? The stress and strain of undressing her!!

MIDDLE 1900'S

In the Great Depression, most people couldn't afford fancy clothes even if they wanted them. In fact, one third of the nation was in rags.

Dad, who are those awful people in those terrible clothes?
They're called "Oakies!" They're poor farmers who can't grow anything on their parched soil, and they're starving to death!
What will happen to them?
Someday they'll have GOOD SOIL and the Government will pay them NOT to grow anything on it . . . and they'll all be MILLIONAIRES!

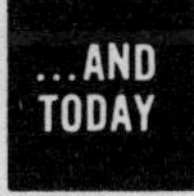

We've got problems today, but there's still a lot of affluence in the land. So how come now everybody dresses like "Oakies" all the time?!

Why is the Bride so late?
She's having big trouble with her wedding outfit!
Really? What happened??
She put her Levi's in the washing machine ten times already . . . and they still won't fade!

PREGNANCY

In keeping with the Victorian approach toward sex, whenever a woman learned that she was Pregnant, she'd never come right out and say it. Instead, she'd throw little hints around.

MIDDLE 1900'S

Then, while a husband and wife were still coy about the subject of Pregnancy, at least they acknowledged what they were fumfering about.

Dear . . . I just came from the Doctor's office! I'm going to have a . . . you know!
Wow! Terrific! We're having a . . . you know! Now, honey, take it easy! Lie down! I'll handle everything! Get plenty of rest and don't do a thing!
But, Marvin! The baby's not due for six months!
Oh! Well, in that case, you wanna shovel off the driveway? The snow is getting deep, and I wanna pull in the car!

...AND TODAY

There's very little hemming and hawing ...and everything is on the table...

Hal, I just found out that I'm **pregnant!**
Fantastic, honey! That's **great news!** Just think! We've been trying and trying for over **ten years** . . . and it's **finally happened!** I couldn't be **happier!** Er . . . when is the baby **due** . . .?
In six months.
Terrific! When do you want to get **married? Before** . . . or **after** . . .?

MONEY

EARLY 1900'S

In those days, there was only one thing to do with money: Save it.

MIDDLE 1900'S

Well, the Son did exactly as his Father had advised and put the $5000 in a bank! Then, 40 years later, on HIS Son's 18th birthday:

...AND TODAY

Well, the Son obeyed his Father's wishes and put the $13,000 in the bank. Then, 26 years later, the Son told the story to HIS Son and gave him the money, now grown to $20,000...

Here, Son, and there's a lesson in **thrift** you can learn from that original $5000! Do you know what $20,000 can **buy** today?
Yeah! About what **$5000** could buy **65 years ago!**
But if your Grandpa had **bought** a Stutz Bearcat instead of putting that $5000 in the bank, what would **you** have **now . . .?**
An **antique automobile** worth about **$45,000!!**
One thing **I can't stand** is a **smart-ass kid!!**

DEATH

During this period, the subject of Death was avoided, and if it ever was discussed, it was treated like some beautiful, mysterious thing.

I have something to **tell** you all! Dear **Grandpa** has gone to his **Reward!** Yes, he's **left** this **Vale of Tears,** and he's gone to meet his **Maker** across the **Great Divide!**
Say what you **want** . . . sounds like the ol' boy **CROAKED** to me!

MIDDLE 1900'S

Then, people were more candid about Death. However, the results weren't much better.

Mom, I've got some **terrible** news . . . **Grandma** just died!
Oh, **no!!** Why **her!?** She was so **young!** She had so much to **live** for! Life is **cruel!** She was **everything** to me! She **raised me** as a girl! She **nursed** me . . . **fed** me—
Hold it, Mom . . .! Not **YOUR** Mother! **DAD's** Mother!!
Oh, well . . . when you **gotta go,** you **gotta go!**

Nowadays, things aren't as bad! They're worse!

EARLY ONE MORNING ON A DESERT ISLAND

D. MARTIN...

HOW MUCH IS ON FIRST? DEPT.

If Ernest Lawrence Thayer were still around, he'd probably agree that his "Casey at the Bat" is hopelessly out-of-date. Baseball has changed a lot over the years, and today balls and strikes don't seem nearly as important as negotiations, high salaries and players' fringe benefits. Our National Pastime has become a battle for the Big Money, which means it's time to rewrite "Casey at the Bat" and retitle it

CASEY AT THE TALKS

ARTIST: JACK DAVIS WRITER: FRANK JACOBS

It looked extremely rocky
 for the famous Mudville nine;
The season was upon them
 and the outfield wouldn't sign;
And when Fenwick turned free agent
 and Moran went into flicks,
The owners shook their heads and moaned
 "We're in a dreadful fix."

They scanned their ledgers gloomily
without a hint of cheer;
The falling season-ticket sales
foretold a losing year;
They clung to one small, distant hope,
an optimistic dream—
The fans would pack the stands
with mighty Casey on the team.

For Casey was a superstar
that any club would prize,
Who last year led the league in hits,
home runs and RBIs;
For months the phone-calls made to him
were scornfully declined;
A god he was, unreachable
and, what was worse, unsigned.

Then from an outer corridor
there rose a mighty shout;
It rattled the reception desk
and shook the walls throughout;
It thundered through the offices
in one tremendous roar,
For Casey, mighty Casey,
was advancing through the door.

There was pride in Casey's manner,
there was class in Casey's style,
As he touched each owner's hand
and gave a patronizing smile;
He'd brought with him six solemn men,
their faces grim and grave—
Two lawyers, three accountants
And his business agent, Dave.

The owners lauded Casey's clothes,
extolled his wavy hair;
They kissed the leather of his shoes
and knelt beside his chair;
They laid before him fruit and wine
and then a full-course meal,
But Casey merely raised his hand
and murmured, "What's your deal?"

"One million bucks is yours," they said,
"for playing out the year,
"Plus 10 percent of grandstand sales
of hotdogs, Cokes and beer;
"When on the road we'll line up broads,
of whom you'll have your choice,
"Plus shares of stock, a butler
and a custom-built Rolls-Royce."

The smile is gone from Casey's lips,
his countenance is stern;
He grips his chair with knuckles white,
he gives his head a turn;
And now he flicks an eyebrow
at his agent standing by,
And now the air is shattered
by the words of his reply.

Oh, somewhere in the baseball world
there is a happy town,
Where management has signed a star
who'll win the triple crown;
And somewhere fans stand up to cheer
a bases-loaded clout,
But there is no joy in Mudville—
Mighty Casey has held out.
CASEY

FATUOUS FIFTIES DEPT.

Have you noticed that people seem to get disgustingly nostalgic about things they weren't really very crazy about in the first place? Like the 50's? We figure that any decade that had the Korean War, the Edsel, Senator Joseph McCarthy, Davy Crockett hats, the Hula-Hoop and Pat Boone wearing fruit boots can't be ALL GOOD! And yet, the hottest show on TV these days is about this very bland, very silly decade where the biggest problem seemed to be *who* was making out with *whom*, and how fast your *face* would clear up. So, okay nerds. Go put on your blue suede shoes, your pedal pushers, your ankle slave bracelets and your leather jackets and get yourselves arrested for committing an idiocy while reading

CRAPPY DAYS

ARTIST: ANGELO TORRES WRITER: ARNIE KOGEN

Joinie . . . will you please TURN DOWN that blasted Rock 'n Roll music!!!
I can't do that, Dad! It's the THEME SONG of the show!!
Oh, that's right! I forgot! All this dopey 1950's teenage music sounds the same to me! Why can't you kids listen to some decent ADULT music . . . like Florian Zabach playing "The Hot Canary"!
By the way, where's your brother, Itchie?
He's up in his room!
Doing what?
Reading some new magazine that has a really wild centerfold!
That's good! As long as he isn't reading that terrible new "MAD Magazine"! It could warp his mind!!
DAILY MIRROR
SENATORS WIN
DAILY MIRROR
IKE SAYS

Hi, Dad!
Oh . . . Hi, Itchie! Where are you off to tonight?
I'm just gonna hang loose and do some typical '50's teenage things! First, I'm gonna stuff a telephone booth! And then I'm going up to Inspiration Point, where all the guys make out!
I see! Uh . . . you got a girl??
No . . . but I have this new magazine that has a really wild centerfold!
BOY
Gosh, what a goofy mixed-up generation of kids! I—I can't believe it!! Hula-hoops!! Stuffing telephone booths!! They're all such suckers for FADS!!
Now, don't get upset, dear! You know the Brewsters are coming over later!
Oh, that's right! It should be a fun evening! I'll show them our new Bomb Shelter . . . and then we'll play some Canasta!
I'd better rush! I want to take a Toni Home Permanent! Where's the Chlorophyl Toothpaste?

Anything wrong, Itchie? How come you're still moping around here?
Dad . . . can I speak to you about a problem?
Is it serious?
Not very! It—it's just that I don't have a DATE for the "SOCK HOP COSTUME BALL"!
On THIS show, that's SERIOUS!!
I don't know, Dad! Something weird is happening to me . . . career-wise! In every '50's film, I used to be the most popular teen-age symbol around! And now, I seem to be losing it all!
Nonsense, Itchie! We all love you . . . even more than ever!
YOU do! But the girls in school . . . and the audience out there . . . THEY DON'T! Someone ELSE is taking my place!!
Itchie, the audience out there watches this show because they like to live in the past! They DIG NOSTALGIA!
So do I! Boy, am I nostalgic for the "good old days"!!
When were the "good old days"?
About two years ago . . .when I was the Star of this show!

Well, whoever this person is, if he's more popular than YOU, he must be very well-mannered, articulate and intelligent!
HEY-YAYYYYY!! It's the FUNZ!!
Then again, maybe I could be wrong!!
Sorry the Funz is late . . . but I was having my hair styled down at the Texaco Station!
At the Texaco Station?!
Yeah! They move my head up and down under the grease rack! HEY-YAYYYY!! WOAH-OHHHH!!

What are you doing with all your suitcases, Funzie??
HEY-YAYY! Funny, you should ask! Since I'M the STAR of the show now, I'm movin' into Itchie's room! Let HIM sleep over the garage!

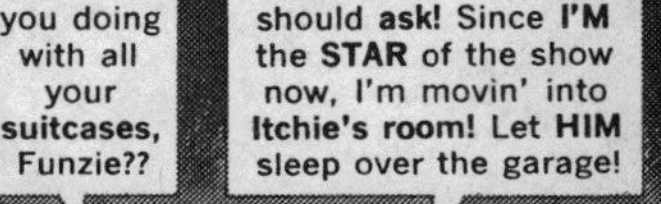

This fugitive from a leather factory is America's new "Cult Hero"!?! Tell me, WHY is the Funz so popular?!?
Because he's pure 1950! He represents the sex appeal of Elvis Presley, the charisma of Marlon Brando . . . and, in all probability, the staying power of Snooky Lanson!
I still don't get what all the fuss is about! To me, he looks like the fashion coordinator for a rumble!
HEY-YAYY! WOAH-OHH!
The Funz'll pretend he didn't hear that remark!
Say, Funz! What's with the "Hey-yayy" and the "Woah-ohh"?
The Funz is the coolest, and that's HIS SOUND! That shows he's cool and tough!
On the other hand . . . it could be gas! That shows he drinks lots of Cokes!
How would you like a knuckle sandwich, Cullingham?!?

Come on, now! Relax, Funzie! Why don't you take off your jacket and make yourself at home?

HEY-YAYY!! Easy, Mrs. C! The jacket STAYS ON!! Where the Funz goes, the threads go! The Funz has worn this same outfit for over three years now!

We KNOW, Funz! We've been meaning to TALK to you about that! It's starting to get a little—shall we say—GAMEY!

And how would YOU like a knuckle sandwich, Mrs. C?!?

Gee, Funzie, I'm in a bind! I don't have a date for the Sock Hop Costume Ball, and I really want to go!

How do you do it, Funz? What's your secret . . . ?

Cool it, Cullingham! The Funz'll get you one of HIS chicks!!

Le'me tell you the Funz's philosophy about women! A woman is like a car! Check 'er out frequently, kick 'er once in a while, and keep 'er locked in a garage!

Wow! What wisdom!! And they say Adlai Stevenson is the egghead of the fifties!

Look! All the **nerds** are here!
Hi, Putzie! **Hi,** Riff!
Hi, fellas! I was just telling **Putzie** about this **chick** I picked up at the **movies!** I took her up to **Inspiration Point** . . . and had a **"perfect night"!**
Yeah! A **"perfect night"!** He went **0** for **9** in **makeout attempts!**

Oh, **yeah!** And I'll bet **YOU'RE some smooth operator!**
Hey . . . are you **cruisin'** for a **bruisin'?!**
Ahh, drink your **soup** before it **clots!**
Har de **har har har!**
I wish the decade would **end** already! I can't stand any more of this **insane 1950's lingo!**
MANDUCK
WON TON U

Hey, who wants a Coke?
I do!
Me too! But I don't have the money!!
You don't need any money! You're with the FUNZ!!

KLONG

CLUNK CLANK

Here ya are! Live it up!!
Y'know, if I didn't have a shoe repair shop on the side, I'd go bankrupt!!

Wow! Look! Arnerd's cheeseburgers are now up to 18 cents! Maybe we ought to try a hangout that doesn't have such "ritzy" prices!
I noticed this new hamburger joint that just opened up down the road! It's got a sign . . . "Over 920 sold"
Ahh! Sounds like another of those fly-by-night '50's "gimmick" places!! What's it called?
McDonald's!!
ALFRED U
STAT

Tell me honestly, Cullingham . . . what do you think of the Funz's "D.A."??
Gee, I'm kinda square, Funz! What does "D.A." stand for?
DON'T ASK . . . !!

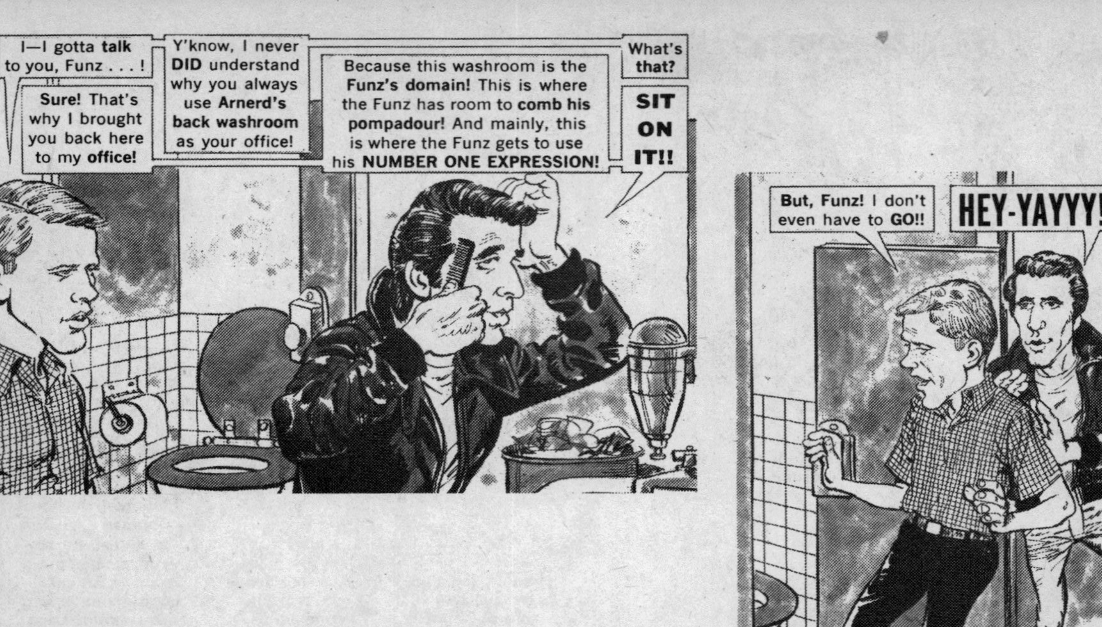
I—I gotta talk to you, Funz . . . !
Sure! That's why I brought you back here to my office!
Y'know, I never DID understand why you always use Arnerd's back washroom as your office!
Because this washroom is the Funz's domain! This is where the Funz has room to comb his pompadour! And mainly, this is where the Funz gets to use his NUMBER ONE EXPRESSION!
What's that?
SIT ON IT!!
But, Funz! I don't even have to GO!!
HEY-YAYYY!!

Sorry! I didn't mean to be a nerd! Okay, I'll just sit here and we'll chat! I—I was wondering if you got me a date for the Sock Hop Costume Ball?
Just leave it to the Funz, Itchie! You got it made in the shade!
Funz, you're the King of the Cool!
Oh, yeah?! Well, if I'm the King, how come YOU'RE on the THRONE?!
SIT ON IT
PUCHI LOVES WANDA
KILROY WAS HERE
Well, here we are . . . chaperoning the Sock Hop Costume Ball!
Yeah! I just LOVE getting out of the house and into some silly costume! Have you noticed . . . they DO this to us every three or four shows?!
Are you embarrassed?
Don't be ridiculous! I ENJOY going down to the Paramount Wardrobe Department and ordering a "44 STOUT BUNNY SUIT"!

Splish, splash, I was taking a bath, long about Saturday night—
It's a good thing we're here! There's no telling WHAT they'd be doing if we weren't watching!
What a generation! Making out after only three dates! Wearing hip-huggers! Sneaking off and smoking king-size cigarettes . . . !!
Teenagers will NEVER get any wilder than they are now!
Why can't they be honest, upstanding citizens like Vice President NIXON?!
It's those "Esquire Magazines" and those controversial Beach Movies! They should be BANNED!!
When your sweetheart sends a letter of good-bye—
Say! In what EXACT year is this show taking place . . .?!
Because I'm all mixed up! They just played "Splish Splash". . . a hit from 1958! And now they're playing "Cry". . . a hit from six years EARLIER in the '50's!!
Whatever is convenient for the show! Why?
Okay, so we'll dance backwards!

Hi, Itchie! You having fun?!?
Not really, Dad! Funzie hasn't shown up with my date yet, and I've been dancing alone all evening!
Well . . . don't blame the Funz! It's hard getting a partner when you're dressed as a PORCUPINE!!

It's about time you showed up, Funzie! Where's my date . . .?!?
She'll be right in!
I can't wait!! Is she really keen-looking?!
Itch, she's the most sensational thing in a dress in the entire decade! She's the RAGE of the '50's! When she walks in, you won't be able to take your eyes off her! You won't be able to CONTROL yourself!!

I thwear . . . I'll kiwwl you a miwwlion times . . .

Uncle MILTY is my date for the Sock Hop Costume Ball ?!? Why, Funzie? WHY?
'Cause that's the Funz's JOB on this show, you nerd, you!
WHAT?!? To bring on some Comedian in DRAG?!
No, clod, to pull in the RATINGS!! And in the '50's, Uncle Milty is NUMBER ONE in the RATINGS!!

Well, I gotta be going now! I'm off to my new '50's job: "Valet Car Stripping!"
Funz, why don't you settle down and straighten out?!? You know . . . America is the land of opportunity for the right kind of men!!
I know! That's why I'm staying EXACTLY where I am, Mr. C.!!
How come . . . ?!?
In what other country can a man like me . . . in his 30's . . . make a million bucks playing the part of a 19-year-old . . . giving everyone "The Finger"?!?
HEY-YAYYY!!
WOAH-OHHH!!

Holy cow!! Look what just walked into our show! A—a BLACK kid!
Not yet!! I'm still a NEGRO! I won't be a BLACK for another ten years! In fact, it's been only five years since I was COLORED!
LAS VEGAS PREP

There must be some mistake! Blacks aren't on television in the '50's!
I KNOW!! But I think I'll just wait around here at the dance!!
Wait?!? For what . . . ?!
For the '70's, you jive turkey!!
That's when ME and my FRIENDS take over!
Hey, Sanford! Is it okay to come in?
Sure thing, Jefferson! And bring Florida and the rest!!!
LAS VEGAS PREP
P

REACHING FOR NEW "HYPES" DEPT.

Because of today's inflation, most magazines are in severe financial trouble. Except, of course, MAD. (We were in severe financial
rouble before inflation!) And so, in order to effectively boost
agging sales, many of the "specialty" magazines are broadening
heir subject matter to appeal to a much wider range of reader
nterest. A quick glance at these covers will show . . .

HOW "SPECIALTY MAGAZINES" ARE TRYING TO BOOST SALES

ARTIST:
JACK
RICKARD

WRITER:
DICK
DE BARTOLO

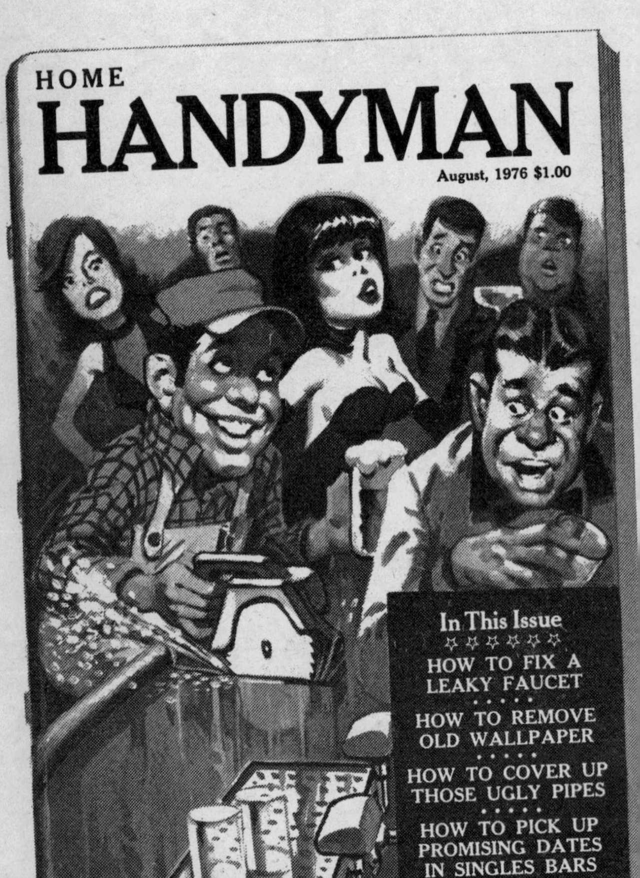
HOME
HANDYMAN
August, 1976 $1.00
In This Issue
HOW TO FIX A LEAKY FAUCET
HOW TO REMOVE OLD WALLPAPER
HOW TO COVER UP THOSE UGLY PIPES
HOW TO PICK UP PROMISING DATES IN SINGLES BARS

MODEL BUILDER
The Hobbyists Magazine
August, 1976
ONE DOLLAR
FEATURING
5 Authentic New
TRAIN MODELS
* * *
7 Intricate New
SHIP MODELS
* * *
6 Detailed New
PLANE MODELS
* * *
4 Accurate New
CAR MODELS
PLUS
10 Exciting New
NUDE MODELS
A Full Color
Pictorial Section

BLACK BELT ILLUSTRATED
September 1976
$1.00
IN THIS ISSUE
You Too Can Have
FISTS OF DEATH
•
FEET OF DESTRUCTION
•
MUSCLES OF STEEL
•
FINGERS OF POWER
•
FILLET OF SOLE
6 Dynamite Recipes

AUTO
TREND
August, 1976
One Dollar
TESTING THE LATEST TRANSISTORIZED IGNITION SYSTEMS
EVALUATING THE
SYNTHETIC OILS
A REPORT ON THE
$16,000 CADILLAC
DRIVING YOUR CAR TO THE BOWLING ALLEY
100 Ways To Improve Your Bowling Score
Which Bowling Shoes Are Best For You
A Guide To Alleys Open 24-Hours A Day

JOKE & DAGGER DEPT.

SPY

Prohias.

FLAG ON THE PLOY DEPT.

NFRACTIONS

WE'D LIKE TO SEE CALLED IN EVERYDAY LIFE

ARTIST: JACK DAVIS WRITER: PAUL PETER PORGES

THE INFRACTION:

THE CALL:

"Holding"

THE PENALTY:

Having To Listen To One's Own Drivel For A Whole Evening

THE INFRACTION:

THE CALL:

"Piling On"

THE PENALTY:

Being Barred From Use Of The Bathroom For Duration Of Event

THE INFRACTION:

THE CALL:

"Tripping"

THE PENALTY:

One 340-Pound Return Stomp

THE INFRACTION:

THE CALL:

"Pushing"

THE PENALTY:

Being Forced To Miss The Next Two Commuter Busses

THE INFRACTION:

THE CALL:

"Interference
—By Grandma"

THE PENALTY:

Having To Spend One Week Alone
With The Little Darlings

THE INFRACTION:

THE CALL:

"Fouling"

THE PENALTY:

Enforced Exposure During Heat Of Summer

THE INFRACTION:

THE CALL:

"Passing To An Illegal Receiver Downfield"

THE PENALTY:

Insufficient Tip

THE INFRACTION:

THE CALL:

"Too Much Time Out"

THE PENALTY:

Garlic Breath From Next Five Patients

THE INFRACTION:

THE CALL:

"Too Much Time In The Huddle"

THE PENALTY:

Having To Spend Remainder Of Evening With Her Parents

THE INFRACTION:

THE CALL:

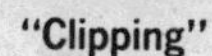

"Clipping"

THE PENALTY:

Internal Revenue Audits Of
Five Years Of Overcharging

DON MARTIN DEPT.

ONE FINE MORNIN

N A

PLAY PEN

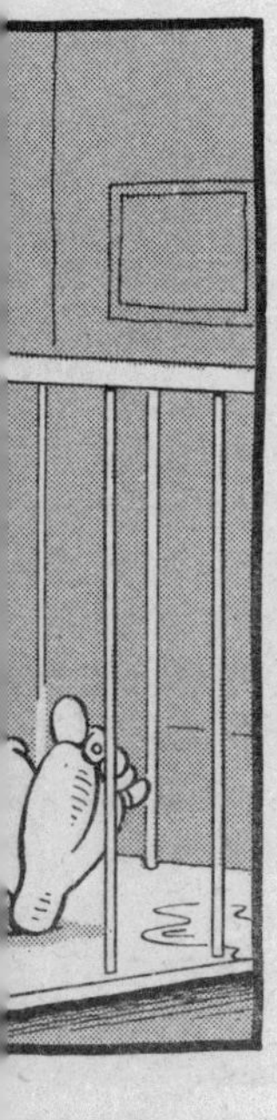

This is little **Tina** from **next door**! She's come over to **play** with you!

Isn't she **sweet** . . . ?!?
PAT PAT PAT PAT

And **look!!** She's brought along her **brand new rattle**

Isn't that cute . . . ?!?
CHAKA
CHAKA
CHAKA
CHAKA

So play nice, now . . .

CHAKA
CHAKA
CHAKA
CHAKA
PAT PAT
PAT PAT
D. MARTIN...

HE JOKE'S ON U.S. DEPT.

Okay, all you clods out there! So you think those "Polish Jokes" that you've been telling are hilarious . . . and you've been breaking up every time you hear how stupid and imbecilic Poles supposedly are?!? Well, we've got news for you! In Poland, they've got *their* favorite jokes . . . about *US*! And so, here, direct from the bars and coffee houses of downtown Warsaw, is the latest selection of . . .

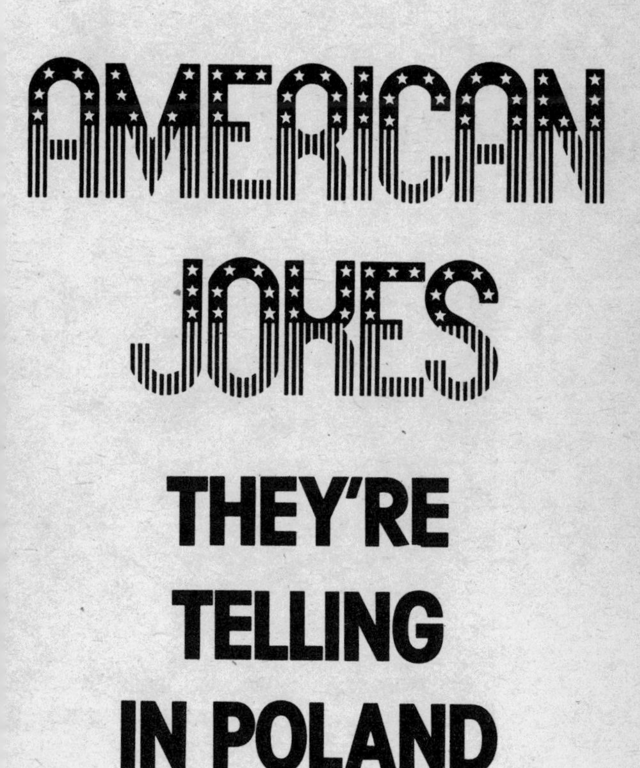
AMERICAN
JOKES
THEY'RE
TELLING
IN POLAND

ARTIST: PAUL COKER, JR. WRITER: FRANK JACOBS

Why does it take 3 Americans to change a lightbulb?
One to stand on the ladder, and two to carry enough lightbulbs until one is found that isn't defective.

How can you tell when it's midnight at an American Airport?
When you the see the 8:00 P.M. flights taking off!

Why do American 18-year-olds take Sex Education Courses?
So they can learn what they've been doing wrong for the past five years!

What's gray, sits on a window sill and hums, and dies mysteriously 91 days after you bring it home?
An American air conditioner with a 90-day warranty!

How many members of "The American Association of Honest Automobile Mechanics" attended last year's convention?
WELCOME!
Both of them!

What's brown and deformed, with its insides hanging out?
A parcel in an American Post Office marked "Fragile"!

What do you call a **TV set** in America that goes **five years** without **need** of **repair?**
UNFAIR
TO AMERKAN
FEDERATION OF
AMALGAMATED
An "**Import**"!

How can you tell when it's **two hours after a terrible American automobile accident?**
By the **arrival** of the **Ambulance!**

What do you call a **letter** mailed in **Dallas** on a **Thursday,**
and arriving in **Ft. Worth** a **week** from the **following Monday?**
"Special Delivery"!

How can you tell when you're
on an **American beach?**
By the **oil slick** in the **water!**

What is the record for the number of late-night strolls through an American urban ghetto?
One!

How can an American be certain that the car he's bought is actually new?
When it's recalled by the factory!

What happened when the American doctor made a house call?
The patient died of shock!

What do American unions call walking off their jobs, striking unlawfully, and crippling an entire city?
SPITAL WORKERS SICK OF WORK
FIREMANS WORK IS NOT SO HOT STRIKE
COPS DESERVE MORE/BETTER
SANITATION WORKERS ON STRIKE FOR MORE SANITARY WORKING CONDITIONS
"Collective Bargaining"!

What's black on the inside, white on the outside, and polluted?
42ND STREET
DOWNTOWN
NEXT RIGHT
Any large American city!

What's the most popular American humor magazine?
MAD Magazine!
What kind of an American Joke is THAT?!?
The biggest one of all!!
MAD
Yecchski!

"SNOW" BIZ DEPT.

There's one thing that can be said about American advert
ing: It may confuse you, unnerve you, infuriate you or bo
you . . . but it cannot flagrantly lie to you. That's because v
have "Truth-In-Advertising" laws that prevent manufactu
ers from making wild claims of excellence for worthle
junk. But one huge industry remains that can still legally r
false and misleading ads to palm off defective products
unsuspecting clods. MAD envisions that great day . . .

WHEN
"TRUTH-IN-
AI

ARTIST: BOB CLARKE WRITER: TOM KOCH

VERTISING"
LAWS
APPLY TO
MOVIE ADS

"INCREDIBLY CONCEIVED . . . A STIRRING ENDEAVOR . . . WELL DONE"

—The Hollywood Supporter

(As required by the Truth-In-Advertising Law, the full statement of the reviewer from which this edited version is taken is as follows:

"This picture is an incredibly conceived bungle which makes mish-mosh of a stirring endeavor in military history. As viewed by this critic, it comes across as nothing more than yesterdays well done goulash.")

"A MONUMENTAL UNDERTAKING . . . THIS MOVIE STANDS OUT . . . GREAT ACTING TALENT . . ."

—St. Louis Post Disgust

(As required by the Truth-In-Advertising Law, the full statement of the reviewer from which this edited version was taken is as follows:

"Sitting through this clinker proved to be a monumental undertaking. Sad to say, this movie stands out as a glaring example of the waste of supposedly great acting talent on a script that is truly awful.")

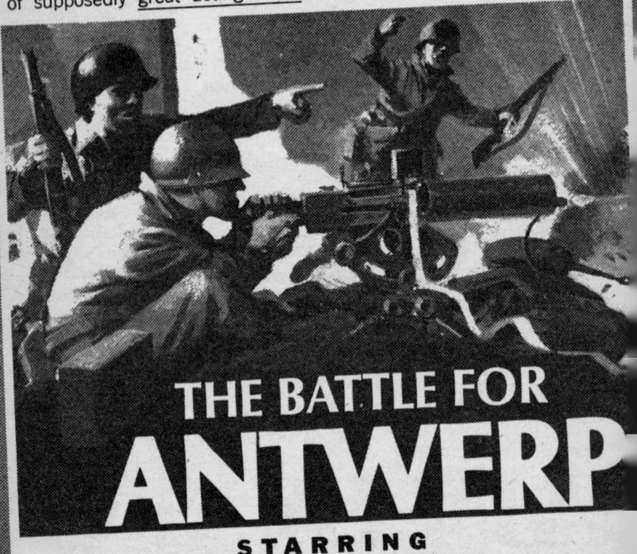

STARRING

CHARLTON HESTON

who always demands star billing even though he only makes a cameo appeara that lasts for 30 seconds or so, which means that the film actually featu

MAX BANGHORN LILY THWANK HOBART STAFFLE CLAUDE RUMLY & EDITH BLUX as T B-

ONE OF THE YEAR'S BEST EROTICA FEATURETTES[1]

2

Starring All Your Favorites from Our Porno Classic, "Clutched Throat"[3]

Rated XXX
Absolutely
No One Under
18 Admitted[4]

"WILD TEEN-AGE MASSEUSES"[5]

FILMED IN PORNO-VISION[6]

A TOUCHING MOVIE EXPERIENCE YOU'LL NEVER FORGET[7]

IN COMPLIANCE WITH THE MOVIE "TRUTH-IN-ADVERTISING" LAW, THE FOLLOWING MANDATORY FOOTNOTES TO THIS AD ARE PRESENTED

1. "Erotica Featurette" is the term used to describe any dirty movie that runs for less than 20 minutes and doesn't have a shred of plot.
2. The attractive model featured here does not appear in the movie. The girls in the movie are all much fatter, more ugly and have acne.
3. This includes the man who wears the black socks to bed, the woman with the tattoo and the sweaty guy who portrays the hotel desk clerk.
4. Unless he can come up with enough money for an admission ticket.
5. The average age of the girls is 38, but all are former teenagers.
6. "Porno Vision" is a catchy name to describe grainy black & white.
7. Getting touched for $6 to sit on a broken folding chair and watch this movie is, we think, an experience that no one could ever forget.

THE YEAR'S MOST SHOCKING FILM!

(But only in the opinion of the Producer and the Director who were both shocked because they thought it would turn out much better than it did.)

SEE IT FROM THE BEGINNING!

(That's because those who enter the theater after it starts risk being trampled by the angry people storming out to demand their money back.)

YOU'LL WANT TO TELL YOUR FRIENDS!

(What are friends for, if not to tip each other off about these bombs?)

OVERWHELMING IN ITS POWER!

(Comparison tests prove that only tainted fish washed down with Scotch and Root Beer can make you throw up as violently as this picture will.)

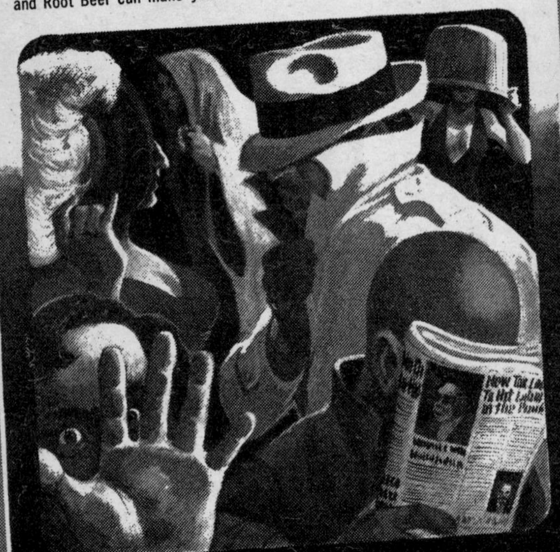

"The Bad Scene"

STARRING

NUMEROUS PROFESSIONALS WHO'VE ASKED THAT THEIR NAMES NOT BE MENTIONED

THIS AD HAS BEEN PREPARED SO IT CLEVERLY COMPLIES WITH THE MOTION PICTURE TRUTH IN ADVERTISING LAW

FOR THE FIRST TIME EVER,
ONE FILM
SWEEPS THE ACADEMY AWARDS IN ALL FIVE MAJOR CATEGORIES*

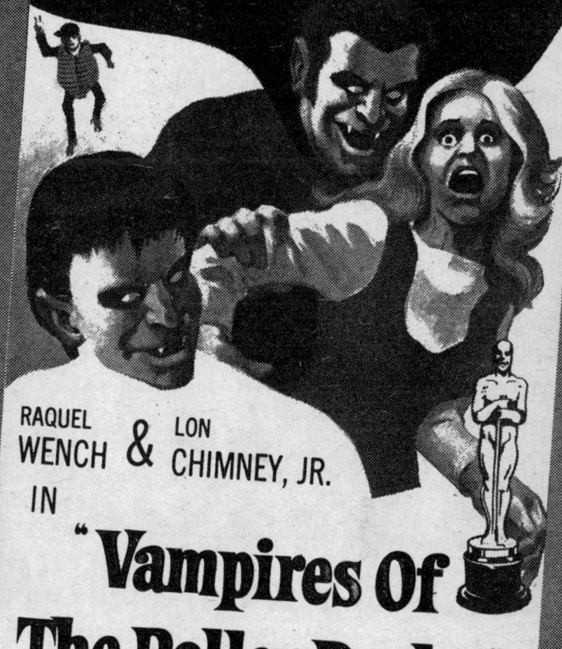
RAQUEL WENCH
&
LON CHIMNEY, JR.
IN

"Vampires Of The Roller Derby"

*Truthfully, we had to convince ourselves that "Best Picture" and "Best Actor" are just MINOR Academy Awards before we became certain that we had swept all of the MAJOR categories by winning these five:

1. Best Sound Effects In A Mob Scene Of Three People
2. Best Film Splicing Done With Ordinary Scotch Tape
3. Best Foreign Sub-Titles For Overseas Distribution
4. Best Costumes On A Budget Of Less Than $1000.00
5. Best Mimeographing Of A Feature Length Film Script

WAS WATERGATE A PLOT TO DESTROY AMERICA?

WERE DEMENTED MANIACS RUNNING OUR COUNTRY?

In all honesty, the Producers of this film don't think so. But then, sitting way out here in Hollywood, how the heck would we know? All we're interested in, quite frankly, is using sensationalism to make a fast buck. So if you'd like to help us achieve our goal...

YOU MUST SEE THIS MOTION PICTURE!

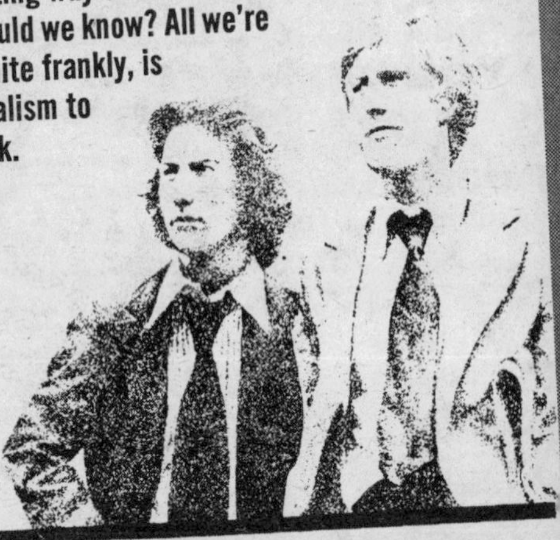

H. R. REDFORD / G. DUSTIN HOFFMAN

"ALL THE WHITE HOUSE FLUNKIES"

WITH E. JASON ROBARDS as E. HOWARD HUNT

NOTE: THE MINOR PARENTHETICAL INSERTIONS IN THIS AD WERE MADE BY OUR CLEAN CUT, PATRIOTIC EXECUTIVES AT WALT DIZZY PRODUCTIONS TO COMPLY WITH THE "TRUTH-IN-ADVERTISING" LAW. NOW, WE URGE YOU TO EXERCISE YOUR RIGHTS AS AMERICANS BY REFUSING TO READ THESE INSERTS WHICH THE #$%@ @#$! WASHINGTON BUREAUCRATS ARE FORCING US TO RAM DOWN YOUR THROATS.

FUN FOR THE WHOLE FAMILY!

(Assuming everyone in your family is under the age of 5)

YOU WILL LAUGH OUT LOUD!

(If you're the type that normally laughs out loud at the mere sight of a tousle-haired freckle-faced child actor)

MORE AMUSING THAN "FANTASIA"!

(Which we feel safe in saying because most of you are too young to remember that "Fantasia" wasn't at all amusing)

DONE AS ONLY DIZZY CAN DO IT!

(Unless you realize that other studios certainly could do it the way we do if thev chose to drop down to our level)

"SCRUFFY AND THE FLASHER"

The Touching Story Of A Boy And His Turtle

STARRING:

SOME CHILD ACTOR WHO WILL EXPERIENCE A METEORIC RISE TO STARDOM, FOLLOWED BY A METEORIC FALL TO OBLIVION

&

SOME OVER-THE-HILL STAR WE RESURRECTED FOR THIS BOMB BECAUSE HE COULD BE HAD CHEAP

WE SHOULD LIVE SO LONG DEPT.

WE'D LIKE TO SEE THE DAY WHEN...

ARTIST: JACK DAVIS WRITE: LOU SILVERSTONE

...there are as many cops on our streets as there are on our TV's.

...mail service improves instead of getting worse every time they raise postage rates.

...it's illegal for relatives of any politician to be on government payrolls.

...a Club Owner fires all 25 players and keeps the Manager.

. . . the head of a municipal union announces that his men will take a cut in pay to help a city that's going broke.

. . a person has to pass a test and get a license to own a gun ust like he does to drive a car or get married or any other angerous undertaking.

. . . theaters that raise prices when they show biggies like "The Godfather" cut prices when they show a bomb.

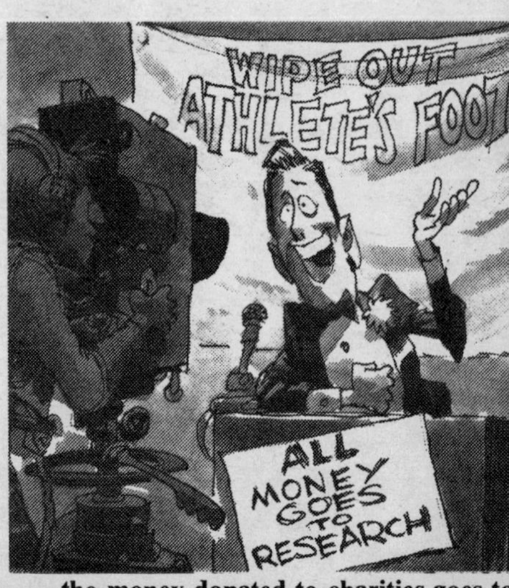

. . . the money donated to charities goes to the charities instead of the fund-raisers.

. . . a President doesn't spend the last two years of his term running for re-election.

. . . those radicals who sneer at the Establishment make it on their own without food stamps, welfare or ripping off people.

**...the coach of a "football factory" turns down a bowl bi
because his players have already missed too many classes**

**...politicians who break the law
are treated like any other crooks.**

...the people have a right to vote on the pay raises and gravy train benefits of their elected officials.

..the companies that make millions selling pet food donate some of that bread to help feed and shelter homeless animals.

ONE WEDNESDA

IN

VENING
ESTAURANT
MEN'S ROOM

EMPLOYEES
MUST WASH
HANDS BEFORE
RETURNING
TO WORK

RG'S-EYE VIEW DEPT.

THE LIGHTER SIDE OF...

ARTIST & WRITER:
DAVE BERG

SURPRISE!!
Oh, my goodness! This is, indeed, an unexpected surprise!

I want to thank my friends, my relatives and especially my dear sweet Husband for remembering my birthday . . .
. . . which was LAST MONTH

Here's your birthday present, Daddy . . .
Thank you!
Oh, my . . . it's a lovely shirt with the initials "D.K." on it! Er—D.K.?!?
D.K.
But, Sweetheart! My name is ROGER Kaputnik! My initials are R.K.! What's the "D" for?
"DADDY"!!

Please, Tom . . . my parents are liable to walk in!
They won't be home for hours!

WHAT'S GOING ON HERE?!?

It—it's all right, Mom! We're engaged!
Okay!! So you're engaged!!

BUT IN WHAT?!?

Vivian, I'd like you to meet my dear old friend, Charlie McGilla!
Excuse me, but this "dear old friend" of yours is NOT named Charlie McGilla! It's Al Glinker!

Er—uh . . . of course it is! How could I—Marty Finster—be so scatter-brained?!? Well . . . I'll see you around, Charlie . . . I mean, AL . . .!!

Wow! You ARE bad at names! You can't even remember your OWN name! You told him it was Marty Finster! Your name is Milton Blung . . . remember?
I know my own name!!

But I'd much rather he think Marty Finster is a klutz . . . instead of ME!!

O.K.! O.K.! What happened here?
This lunkhead crashed into my rear fender just as I was making a right turn!!
It was all her fault! She . . . she SIGNALED!!
Oh . . .? And she gave the WRONG signal?
No, she gave the RIGHT signal . . .!!
That's what CONFUSED me

Waiter, do you have a match . . .?
No, sir . . . but I'll get one for you!

The gentle-man at table four would like a match!
A MATCH?! This is a fine restaurant with fine patrons! Matches are gauche! You should carry a fancy lighter so you can service our customers! Here— you can borrow mine!

Here you are, sir!
What good is THAT?!?

I can't pick my TEETH with a LIGHTER!!

Do you know how much of our income taxes goes to paying Welfare?! Okay, we should take care of our indigent!

But I resent paying for those BROOD SOWS who keep knocking out one illegitimate kid after another!

HOW DARE YOU CALL A WOMAN A "BROOD SOW"!! NO PERSON SHOULD BE COMPARED TO AN ANIMAL, YOU MALE CHAUVINIST—

—pig?

Hello, Mary Lou! I'm calling to invite you for a ride on my new boat! And you really can't turn me down! After all, I did name it AFTER YOU!
You DID?! In that case, I'll come!

Hey, Buddy-boy! You are in big trouble! I mean, how many times can you use the same line? Just a minute ago, I heard you tell Ginny the same thing you told Mary Lou!
"After all, I did name it AFTER YOU!"

Man, what are you gonna do when they both get here?!?
There's no problem, Fella! You haven't seen my new boat yet! Take a look—

AFTER YOU

Can I help you, Daddy? Huh? Can I help??
Yes, you can! I need a SCREWDRIVER very badly!

One screwdriver . . . coming up!!

What's taking you so long?!
I've got problems!

I found the ORANGE JUICE! But where's the VODKA?!?

WHAT DID YOU SAY?!? That was a dirty filthy four-letter Anglo-Saxon word you threw at me!!

It . . . it just slipped out!
This is a God-fearing, law-abiding home! I don't want to ever hear you use such language again, do you hear!?!

But, Mom! Norman Mailer, Tennessee Williams and Philip Roth use words like that all the time!

I don't care!! In fact, I forbid you to hang around with that gang anymore!!

I can't wait to tell Harriet!!
Hi, Harriet! This is Marion! Have I got dirt for you! You know that Viola Foogle? Well, I just heard her Husband is a Transvestite . . . and she's making it with her Golf Pro! And you know how she claims she's 29?! Well, she's almost 40!
Boy . . . have I got Viola's number!!
You sure DO . . .!
THIS IS VIOLA!!

I GOT IT!!
I GOT IT!!
Now, I'm gonna get it!

Look at me! I'm—I'm FAT! F-A-T—FAT!! For the life of me, I can't lose weight!

I go on diets! Regularly! But after a day of starving, I get so darn hungry, I start stuffing myself!

Excuse me, Lady . . . but I haven't eaten in two days!
Oh, that's marvelous!

I admire your will-power!
David Berg

TELE LIKE IT IS! DEPT.

As if you don't see enough TV on TV, now you can go to the movies and see movies about TV. So stay home, turn off your boob tube, and read this satire instead. It won't do much for you, but it'll save you an admission price and some electricity.

ARTIST: MORT DRUCKER

WRITER: STAN HART

I'm going to get to the top of this ☆#!★ network, and no ☆⑥!★⑥ is going to stop me! I'll show the #⑥☆☾!★# Network Brass that I'm as good as ANY!#★ man!!
But . . . you're NOT!!
What do you mean, you ★⑥☆# ?!?
No man talks as DIRTY as you do!
As a long-time concerned TV Newsman, I say that murders, shootings and rapes do not belong on TV Dramatic Shows!
You mean they offend your moral code?
No . . . my NEWSMAN'S CODE! They belong on TV NEWS SHOWS only!!
I'm a ruthless Network Executive who'll stop at nothing to get good ratings!!
You'll stop at nothing?
That's right! If I thought we could get good ratings, I'd even bring back "The Captain and Tennille"!
Nobody could be THAT ruthless!
UBS
UNSCRUPULOUS BROADCAST SYSTEM INC.

"Nutwork" is the story of how a TV Newsman destroys himself! It's a unique plot!
No, it isn't! Harry Reasoner did it on ABC!
When??
Last year . . . when he agreed to have Barbara Walters as his partner!
This picture is an exposé of the idiotic stupidity of TV!
Who needs it! I see TV exposing stupidity seven nights a week!!
My show's been cancel-led, so I've decided to do something people have never seen on TV! One last futile, but romantic gesture . . .
And what's that?
I'm going to pick my nose before forty million viewers!
You can't do that on TV! It's horrible!
Okay, then, I'll KILL myself on camera!!
NOW you're talking! That's much more acceptable!!

These days, the Networks only want **PRETTY BOYS** to sit there and read the news off idiot cards! It's not like the great **OLD DAYS,** when they had **JOURNALISTS** like **us** sit there and read the news off idiot cards!

You're just experiencing a **depression,** Harrowed! Give it **time** and **you'll** come out of it! I remember a depression **I** had back in **1945** . . .

When did **you** come out of it?

Last Friday!

Okay, here's the line-up for tonight's news show! We've got two-minutes on the sexual assault of a 93-year-old woman, six minutes on a tiger tearing a little girl's arm off, and three minutes of a mother who just found out that all of her kids perished in a school fire!
Only three minutes? We need two more!
No sweat! We get the Mother to sing the school song!
That still leaves us a minute short!
Just enough time for Harrowed Bile to shoot himself on camera!

Impossible! We CAN'T let Harrowed Bile SHOOT HIMSELF!!
But he WANTS to die!
Tell him to swallow a slow poison that takes thirteen weeks to work!
Why THIRTEEN WEEKS?!?
That way, we might get a SERIES out of it!

Folks . . . I'm old, and a drunkard! My wife is dead, and my children hate me! I haven't got a dime to my name, and I've just been fired! So, I am going to kill myself on this show tomorrow!
No! No! You can't do it!
Why not?
Because you have so much to LIVE for!
NBS

We need a **HIT SHOW,** or this @#@!☆ Network is **FINISHED!** Somehow, **our shows** always seem to **miss!**
You mean like **"Little House On The Rockies"** or **"The Two Million Dollar Man"** or **"Happy Years"**!
You bet your !#★@ We need something that will make a **frustrated public ANGRY!**
We could bring back **"Bridget Loves Bernie"**!
Not **THAT** Angry!

We need something like **this!** This is a film of a **terrorist group** dedicated to **destroying America** by driving everyone **insane!** They took this of **themselves** as they actually broke into a **Supermarket . . .**
What are they **doing** in there?
Fixing the **wheels** of **shopping carts** so that no one can steer them straight down the aisles!
Diabolical fiends!

And here they are, attacking the mental health of America's youth by sneaking into our Bubble Gum factories and putting "doubles" and "triples" of San Diego Padre players into baseball card packs!
Depraved wretches . . . !
Now, my idea is to have this terrorist group film one of its militant capers every week, and call the show, "Up Yours, America"!
You have a fabulous mind . . . and a tush to match!!

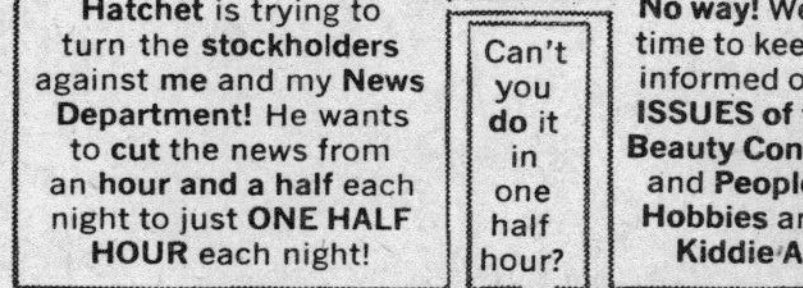
ANNUAL STOCK HOLDER MEETIN
Hatchet is trying to turn the stockholders against me and my News Department! He wants to cut the news from an hour and a half each night to just ONE HALF HOUR each night!
Can't you do it in one half hour?
No way! We NEED that time to keep the public informed on the VITAL ISSUES of the day, like Beauty Contest Winners and People With Cute Hobbies and Adorable Kiddie Art Shows!

Ladies and Gentlemen, I have decided **not** to kill myself tonight! Instead, as a final grand gesture of contempt, I am going to **curse** for five minutes! Starting off the **Top Fifty Dirty Words** is **"COCKY-DOODY"** . . . followed fast by **"PEE-PEE"** and **"EH-EH"** . . .
Quick! Cut him off the air!!
No! **No!** Let him **finish!** He's **getting** to some of my **favorites!**
. . . and who could forget those **oldies** but **goodies, "POO-POO"** and **"WEE-WEE"!**

That was **nasty** and **spiteful** . . . allowing Harrowed Bile to curse on TV! I'm afraid I must ask you to turn in your **key** to the **executive toilet!**
What does **this** mean?
It means you have a **choice!** You can either **leave here gracefully** . . . or you can **explode!**

Here are some **ideas** for **new shows!** This one is about a **middle-aged bald detective** who's a **natty dresser!** This one is about **two young mod cops,** one with a **funny-sounding Polish name!**
No! I want something **different!** Not the **same old things** people can **see** by just looking out their **windows!!**
But these shows have **robberies** and **murders!!** Who looks out their **windows** and sees things like **THAT . . . ?**
The people who live in **Detroit, New York, Chicago** and **every large city** in the **U.S.A.!**
Last night, Harrowed Bile got **fantastic ratings!** That gave me **TWO GREAT IDEAS** for **SHOWS!! One . . . keep Harrowed on!**
No! It's **disgusting** to watch a madman rant and rave!!
But the **public LOVED** it!
So what . . . ?! In **ancient** times, the public loved seeing **Christians** thrown to **LIONS!**
That's my **SECOND idea!!**
The New

Okay, I've changed my mind! You're **NOT** fired! Here's your **toilet key** back . . .
Ah-hah! So you need **allies** in your fight against **Hatchet!**
That's **ONE** reason!
What's the **other?**
Your **office** is starting **to smell something awful!!**

I'd like to **program** the **Harrowed Bile Show!** What do you **say?**
Listen, I feel we could **work REAL HARD** together!
So was I! But at **your** age, it would be **real hard work!**
I ADORE it on **TV . . .** and even **MORE** in my **APARTMENT!**
Hmmmm! You **interest** me!
I was thinking about having a **torried love affair** with you!
Before we start, I'd like to know how you feel about **sex** and **violence!**

Yes! Yes!! I must awaken America! I must tell them the truth! Thank you for enlightening me . . . and for showing me my mission in life!
Oh, and by the way . . . "PANT . . . PANT . . . PANT . . ." to YOU, TOO!!

This is what your News Department was lacking!
Showmanship!
And now, the "Evening News"! With Rocky Stud reporting on the Middle East Crisis . . . while juggling five hoops and three Indian Clubs . . .
CLAP!

. . . and Larry Lawrence reporting on a new outbreak of the Bubonic Plague . . . while being shot out of a cannon . . .

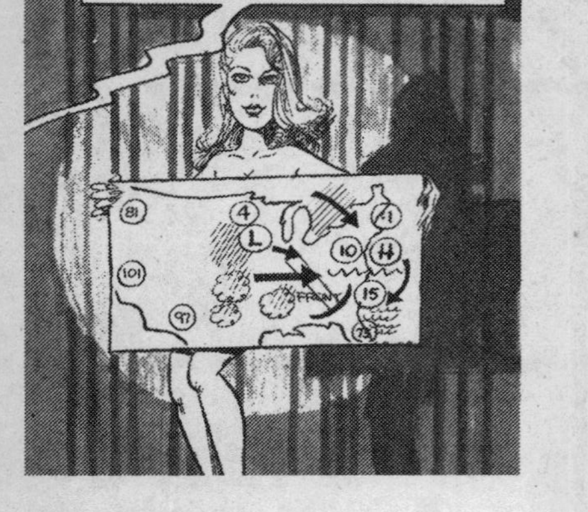
. . . with Linda VaVoom, our "Shower Or Shine Girl" doing her Nude Weather Report . . . and featuring the STAR of our show . . . crazy HARROWED BILE!!

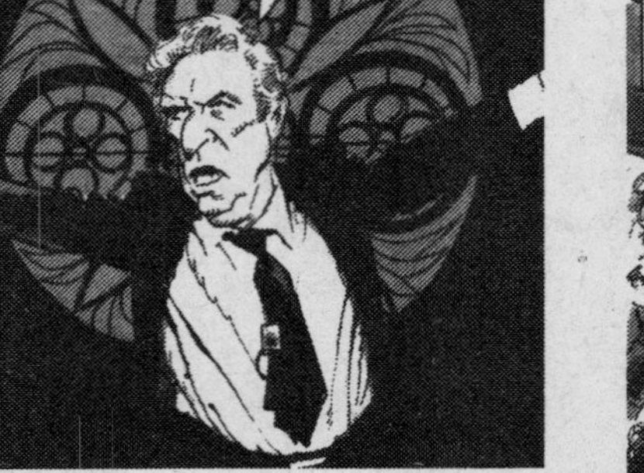
Last night, I received two phone calls, and heard strange voices! The first one said, "Tell America the truth! Tell them that TV is turning them into mindless robots!"
The second was even stranger! It said, "Send up a pizza with extra cheese and pepperoni!"

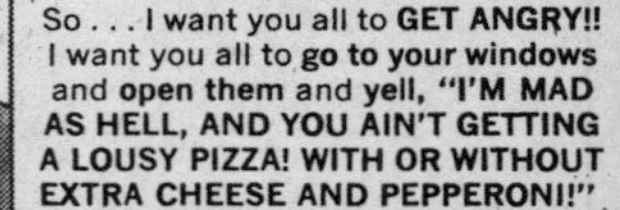
So . . . I want you all to GET ANGRY!! I want you all to go to your windows and open them and yell, "I'M MAD AS HELL, AND YOU AIN'T GETTING A LOUSY PIZZA! WITH OR WITHOUT EXTRA CHEESE AND PEPPERONI!"
UBS

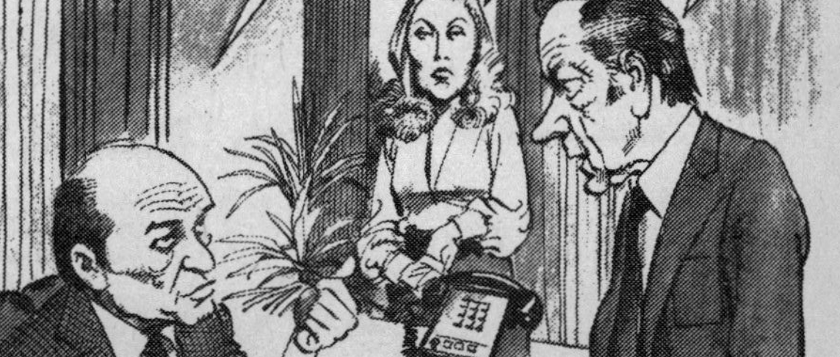
I'M MAD AS HELL, AND YOU AIN'T GETTING A LOUSY PIZZA! WITH OR WITHOUT EXTRA CHEESE AND PEPPERONI!
I'm even madder than they are!
How come?
I'm trying to crack this safe, and I can't hear the TUMBLERS fall with all the YELLING going on!!

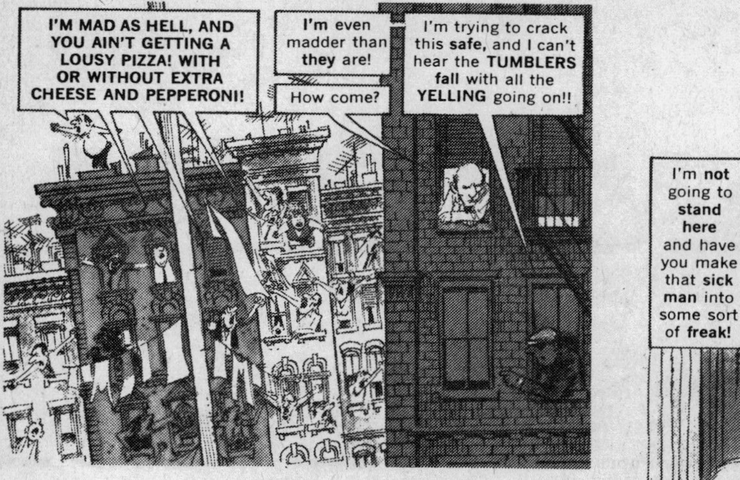
I'm not going to stand here and have you make that sick man into some sort of freak!
I agree! You're NOT going to stand here! You're going to stand out on the street, because you're FIRED!! She's taking over your job!
So . . . you betrayed me, got me fired, ruined my career and destroyed my reputation! And I thought we were FRIENDS!!
Does this mean that we won't have SEX any more?
I was talking about FRIENDSHIP! Who said anything about SEX?!?

So you've decided to run off with a younger woman . . .?
Correct!
Will you show her the same attention and understanding and loyalty you've shown me?
I think so . . .?
Good!! She'll be as miserable as I'VE been all these years!!
I . . . I suppose you think I'm an old fool!
No, I think you're a child!
Why a child?
Because any man who runs off with another woman and asks his wife to sew NAME TAGS on his clothes is a child!

Wake up, America! The Arabs are buying up everything in our country! Soon . . . they'll control it all! If you don't believe me, look out your window . . .

And now, the Arabs are trying to buy
up this very Television Network . . .
CAMELS
ADNAN'S USED CAMELS
RASHID HOTEL
AHMED'S RUGS
ABU SELTZER PLASTIC
SHEIK LINENS
USED CARS CAMELS

My God! He just told about the Arab deal! No one was supposed to know about that! It was a top-level hush-hush project!!
Uh . . do you think he ruined it?
There's a very slim chance it might still go through! It all depends on one IF-y THING!!
What's that?
If forty million Americans can keep a secret!!

You have transgressed, Mr. Bile! You have committed a sin against the most cherished, the most exalted power in the universe!
You mean against GOD?!?
No, against something even more powerful! MONEY!!
But I told Americans—
AMERICANS?!? There are no Americans! There are no Europeans, no Asians! There are no continents, no countries! There is no geography! There is only one thing! MONEY!
Gee, that's terrible! And I spent so much time learning things . . . like the capital of North Dakota!
And what do you think that is . . .?
Bismark!
WRONG!! It's THREE DOLLARS AND SEVENTY-NINE CENTS!
That VOICE!! I—I recognize that VOICE!!
Sure you do! But I could DIE before you'd send up my pizza with extra cheese and pepperoni!
THE UNITED STATES OF AMERICA
F 9102545
WASHINGTON, D.C.
ONE
F 9102535
TONGSUN PARK
KAKUEI TANAKA
ADNAN KHASHOGGI

What do you want me to **do?**
Tell people they **cannot stand in the way of money power!** If you **do** that, you will be on the **path** of **righteousness,** you will be on the **road** to **truth,** and even **MORE IMPORTANT . . .**
What? **What?**
You'll be my **best friend!**

. . . and **so,** my friends, **forget** about **individuality!** Because in our complex world, **individuality** is **doomed . . .!**
Damn him! His messages of gloom are **turning off audiences!**
God, is television **all** that you're **capable** of **thinking** about?! Is TV your **whole reality?!?** I don't know **why** you became involved with me in the **first** place!
Because . . . you **reminded** me of someone **I once loved very much!**
An **old flame?**
No . . . **Captain Kangaroo!**

Bile's ratings are awful! We've got to get rid of him!
The Network Brass wants him to stay on the air! So we can't do anything about it!
I've got a plan! It's very clever . . . and very subtle!
What is it?
We have him KILLED! And I know just the guys who would love to do it!!
Great idea! You have a fabulous mind!
I know! And a tush to match!
It's bad enough we Newsman have to stay on camera all night at our dumb political conventions with nothing to say!
Or have to predict election winners before the polls are even closed!
Or attempt to give truthful news when oil companies and big corporations sponsor our shows!
But having a NUT portray us is TOO much!
ABC
CBS
NBC
ABC
RAT-TAT-TAT-TA